Changing Minds
Home not Hospital

Marina Bowe
Patrick Devitt
Finian Kelly

First published in 2011 by TAF Publishing

ISBN: 978-1-907522-37-6

A CIP Catalogue record for this book is available from the British Library

Cover design and typesetting by Martine Maguire-Weltecke

Published with the assistance of The Author's Friend
For information about Assisted Publishing, including catalogue and titles,
visit www.TheAuthorsFriend.com

Printed and bound in Ireland by Gemini International Ltd

"The mind is its own place, and in itself
Can make a Heaven of Hell, a Hell of Heaven."

Paradise Lost John Milton

This book is dedicated to all our patients,
their families and all who ever worked
in the Clondalkin service

Table of Contents

Acknowledgment

We acknowledge with thanks the Mental Health Commission without whose grant this work would not have been possible.

Foreword

Change doesn't happen on its own. This book describes in a very informative and graphic way, the transition of a local (old) mental health service into a (new) comprehensive community-based service.

Irish mental health services are in transition from the era of the great confinement as described in Chapter 2 of this book, to one which is predominantly community-based, person centred and based on the provision of a range of holistic interventions which promote recovery. This ideal model of service delivery is clearly set out and underpinned in the Government's present mental health policy "A Vision for Change".

Community-based models of mental health service delivery are dependent on a number of important factors;

- Adequate resource allocation to allow change to take place. This includes new resources and the transfer of existing ones.

- Openness by Government and statutory and voluntary service providers to change.

- Flexibility on the part of managers, clinicians and other staff to facilitate change.

- Acknowledgement by patients and family members that community care is desirable.

In any changing environment one can find examples of pioneers who have decided that the existing mode of operation is not adequate and that there needs to be fundamental change. Such local heroes of the Clondalkin service are well described in this book. Their commitment and dedication to change over many many years is a testament to their foresight.

The account is also an illustration of how change can occur as a bottom up process rather than a top down one. Every local service in Ireland is unique. The Clondalkin project is not one to be shamelessly copied by other services. Many of the factors that have made it successful are unique to the service and team members. Other services will have their own unique blend of opportunities and difficulties.

This book is important as an exemplar of how change can occur. It is also important because it not only outlines the thinking and activities of the key professional players but invokes the responses and experiences of mental health care service users and their families, illustrating clearly the positive impact the change has brought to their lives. The value of such a service is encapsulated in the statement of one family member who says;

> "It is amazing that we have access to the doctors and nurses at any time because when things go wrong it is often at night or at weekends when you'd expect them to be off duty but they are always there for us".

This book is required reading for any mental health professional who is contemplating or involved in a change process within their own mental health service.

John Saunders
Director, SHINE – Supporting People Affected by Mental Ill Health

1

It's all so different now

Sheila (not her real name) wants the Irish laws governing involuntary committal to psychiatric hospitals changed as a matter of priority.

"I never want anybody else to go through what happened to me. I was dragged screaming and crying out of my home by the guards, bundled into an ambulance and driven off to St. Loman's. It was horrible, horrible, I will never forget it.

"When we got to St. Loman's I saw my name on the wall. I didn't know what was happening. They tried to talk to me but it didn't work. It was terrible. The person next door to me was shouting and banging. I was in a room on my own, I had no control, my husband, Tom (not his real name) didn't come to see me. I now know he was told not to visit for a while, but at the time I didn't know that. I felt abandoned. I got medication and some counselling, although I didn't know it was counselling at the time.

Sheila's difficulties began 12 years ago with a family upset which left her very depressed. She was just 50 with a good husband and family and had never experienced mental health difficulties previously.

"I was arguing with everybody, particularly Tom and the kids and that's not the way we lived as a family. We used to get on very well and there were never rows before all this began. I thought everybody was against me. My husband tried to get me help but I wouldn't go.

"Then as things got worse, they got a nurse down from the Clinic to speak to me. They probably told me she was from the Clinic but if they did, it didn't get through to me. I didn't know where she was from. I only remember being told that 'this woman's trying to help you.' I think now that if it had been better explained to me, I might have listened. But that didn't happen and I was committed. I think that before anybody is committed, time must be taken to try and explain properly to them, how ill they are and how badly they need help.

"Even now, I couldn't bring myself to visit somebody in Loman's. Now, don't get me wrong, what I'm talking about is the awful building. The staff were brilliant while I was there. They were rushed off their feet but they were very good to us.

"The men and women were on separate sides but sometimes some of the men would drift down to the women's section. I remember one night this guy came down and I thought I wouldn't trust him so I spent the night awake because I was afraid to go to sleep.

"There were funny times too. Because of all the medication you were on, you would always be hungry. I remember when the diningroom doors were opened for meals there would be a mad rush to get in and get to the food.

"When they thought I might be discharged they sent me off in a taxi to spend a day at the Clondalkin Day Hospital. I thought this was great and when I was discharged I attended regularly for two weeks. Then I went on the home care programme where in the beginning a nurse would come out every day to see if I was taking my medication and how I was coping.

"At this time, I wouldn't go outside the door even with my family unless it was in the car. Some of the lads on the estate gave me a bad time. They'd seen me dragged out of my home and into the ambulance and would be shouting and jeering at me. It was summer and they had nothing better to do but hang around the road and the shops. This lasted for a few months and then one day I threatened to set Jessie (her dog) on them and that sorted it out."

Sheila laughs reminiscently. She has a very lively sense of humour and often laughs at herself and others.

"Margaret (Clinic Nurse Margaret Downey) saved me. She is just wonderful. She gave me all this information about mental health. I knew absolutely nothing about mental health and you need to know about it. I can also tell her anything that's worrying me and she understands. We are more like friends than a nurse and a patient.

"Here the doctors and nurses explain your medication to you, how it works and how important it is not to stop taking it because you feel better. If you do, you fall and it's a horrible sensation.

"I come to the clinic every three months and Margaret comes out to me every week. She has taught me the signs to watch out for which mean that I might be going downhill. In the old days I'd sleep very badly. I'd be waking up at all hours of the night. At 2 o'clock I'd have a big burst of energy and I couldn't get back to sleep until 5. My mind would be filled with all my problems. If that happens to me now, I don't wait for the second night. I come straight down to the clinic.

"If I knew 12 years ago, what I know now, I would have gone for help when I needed it. Education and information about mental health are so important. I think the ad on television now is great, it shows how mental illness can effect all groups of people. It's also been highlighted on Fair City, which is good.

"They run meetings here for family members. When I came out of St. Loman's my family were walking on eggshells around me for a while.

"It's hard for young people now. They have an awful lot of financial worries and this is affecting their mental health. I'm really lucky to have my husband and children and the support they give me. It must be hard to live on your own when you're not well. Even in small things, you are inclined to put on weight with the tablets, you have to watch what you eat, they make you want to eat more and if you are living alone you would tend to eat too much. You also have to be very careful not to mix other tablets with your prescription. I wouldn't take a Panadol without checking first with my pharmacist to see if it was all right.

"Here in the clinic they've also taught me how to cope. I've learned to walk away from stress and I know I will be on medication for the rest of my life, but that is not a problem."

Sheila's three children are now married and have moved out of home. She and Tom enjoy visiting them and their grandchildren and having them to visit. "It's great to have them here and great when they go and we love going to their places but we really love coming home again," she laughs.

"I am very lucky in my husband. He has been very good to me and we have a very good life. We have each other, our children and grandchildren. We like to travel and go on holidays. It's all so different now."

2

The Great Confinement

This is the story of the Clondalkin Mental Health Services. In 1989, the service was established as an innovative system of providing care in the community to those individuals suffering from serious mental illness.

Prior to this, indeed over the previous 200 years, those with severe mental illnesses were largely shunned by society and locked up in large institutions. The mid-18th century has been described as "the great confinement".

The numbers incarcerated under the label of mental illness grew and grew until in Ireland, it reached a figure of approximately 21,000 by the end of 1958. There were 20,046 patients in public psychiatric hospitals and a further 1,029 in private hospitals.

In the 1950s, a remarkable event occurred and as is often the case in these matters, by chance. Similar to Alexander Fleming discovering that the growth of bacteria around a particular penicillin mould was retarded, it was noticed by pharmaceutical scientists that a drug, chlorpromazine, used to combat nausea appeared to have a calming effect. Moreover, those phenomena long associated with serious psychotic illness such as hallucinations (false perceptions without a stimulus), delusions (fixed false beliefs without basis in reality) and muddled thinking all appeared to improve.

The full extent of this breakthrough is not as widely recognised as it should be. It really was on a par with the discovery of penicillin and that other great medical breakthrough of the 20th century, hip replacement.

Now that "madness" could be controlled, the institutions to contain madness surely now could be shut down? This simplistic logic led to the "great deinstitutionalisation" of the 1950s, '60s and '70s.

The lack of more sophisticated analysis, of course, caused problems of its own. Psychosocial aspects were not given appropriate attention. Individuals who had spent years, even decades, in strict ordered living conditions were now suddenly released to the community, often bereft of social skills and unable to cope in the community.

Neither had any of these individuals the so-called "insight" into their conditions which would have made them aware of the link between continuing to take medication and remaining symptom-free. The process of deinstitutionalisation failed many and gave rise, in particular in the United States, to the phenomenon known as the "revolving door" and the enforced homelessness of the mentally ill which can still be seen to this day in many American cities, particularly on the west coast.

In 1961, Drs Leonard Stein and Mary Ann Test, attached to the University of Wisconsin, provided the evidence in a funded project that with assertive community follow-up and treatment, individuals with serious mental illness discharged from institutions could be maintained in the community. More than this, these individuals could begin to lead more normal lives in terms of secure housing, meaningful daytime activities, vocational training and assimilation into their local community.

Ironically, having shown the benefit of this Assertive Community Treatment (ACT), the funding for the project was withdrawn and the former pattern reasserted itself.

But the word was out and the work of Stein and Test spawned many similar projects.

Here in Ireland, we were watching carefully what was going on in the UK in particular and also further afield. Ian Falloon was one of the bigger names associated with this type of project which he had initiated in Buckinghamshire. His project not just referred to those discharged from institutions, but could also cater for those who became ill for the first time. It was now possible to treat the acute phase of a first serious psychotic illness in the community without recourse to hospital.

In parallel also, was the development of acute psychiatric inpatient units in general hospitals. Even if an individual could not be managed in the community, admission to a general hospital was less stigmatising, more symptom-focused and shorter.

Falloon's philosophy was to wrap around the mentally ill person whatever supports were needed in their own environment to get them through the acute phase. This even involved mental health staff moving into the person's living quarters and taking on tasks such as cooking and cleaning.

Falloon, himself, was originally from New Zealand to which he returned eventually and it was in the Australian/New Zealand area that much of the innovation with community treatment developed.

Ireland in the 1980s was a depressing place with high unemployment, poor fiscal status and high emigration. According to one of our more famous politicians at the time, Charles Haughey, "We are living beyond our means.", but if we were, this was not reflected in the state of our mental health service infrastructure.

Mental health services were still largely based in and operated from large, mainly Victorian asylums. Psychiatrists in the main were based in the hospital and whatever community involvement existed was rudimentary and usually involved a token community mental health nurse attached to a team which served a specific area (the sector). A clinic was held usually weekly at the central health board clinic within the sector. Otherwise, all activity revolved around the hospital.

In Dublin southwest, the local asylum was St. Loman's Hospital in Palmerstown, six miles from Dublin and not far from the village of Lucan. The building was formerly a TB sanatorium and if not "jerry-built", it was certainly not built in any architecturally tasteful manner and structurally was not designed to last forever.

Taking over from the TB service at the end of the 1950s, this new asylum was designed to cater for the exploding population migrating to the western and south-western suburbs of Ballyfermot and latterly to Clondalkin, Lucan and Tallaght. At its peak, St. Loman's Hospital housed near to 200 patients. Today, there are only seven patients remaining on the campus, much of which has been sold off for development.

The St. Loman's Psychiatric Services, not having its base in a traditionally Victorian asylum, therefore, started its life without the generous infrastructure of the levels of staffing and facilities that were available to other asylums such as St. Ita's and St. Brendan's. As is frequently the case in Irish mental health services, "history is everything." Even today we see services which are very plentiful in staff because these large numbers of staff were needed to service the old asylum.

On that basis, St. Loman's started and remained lean. This and the poor quality of the building may well have been the stimulus to reframe thinking as to how the mental health services would be delivered.

During that time, psychiatry was undergoing somewhat of a renaissance in terms of glamour. Professor Ivor Browne appeared frequently on the Late Late Show begging that the walls of St. Brendan's Hospital be torn down. Psychiatry had infiltrated popular culture. R.D. Laing had written the important book, *The Divided Self*, and Professor Anthony Clare had written *Psychiatry in Dissent*. There was an intellectualism now associated with psychiatry which was overlapping with such disciplines as philosophy, sociology, psychology and game theory.

All this intellectual ferment enticed into psychiatry many bright and idealistic young doctors, one of whom was Dr. Ian Daly.

Ian had joined the St. Loman's service early in the 1980s and in his role as consultant psychiatrist had acquired responsibility for the Clondalkin area.

Clondalkin, a monastic settlement from the 8th century and a rural farming area for the first half of the 20th century, was now a burgeoning population centre. By the mid '80s, it was an area of high unemployment and deprivation with increasing social and drug problems.

Ian Daly is an avid reader with a quick mind and an incisive grasp of new ideas. He quickly absorbed the literature on assertive community treatment. He became enamoured of the idea that Clondalkin could be the first project of this nature in Ireland. He pressed and debated his ideas, eventually wearing down the "powers that be". These included Michael Walsh, the Programme Manager for Mental Health Services in the Eastern Health Board, and also Dr. Dermot Walsh, the Clinical Director of the St Loman's service.

Michael Walsh was an official who had developed the reputation of a "can-do" attitude. He had taken personal responsibility for organising the depletion of the numbers of patients at St. Brendan's Hospital. Once on board, he was able to acquire the necessary finances to launch the "Clondalkin Project".

This book will try and follow the course of the project from its genesis to its operation today. Apart from telling a good story as to how success was achieved over obstacles, we hope it will celebrate the vision, tenacity and skill of the early pioneers. It is important that their story be heard, not just so they can have praise heaped upon them, but also so that others currently languishing in frustration and hopelessness with respect to the state of the Irish mental health services may discover some spark of hope.

The Clondalkin Project has enriched the lives of those suffering with mental illness in the local community and it has done so while preserving autonomy and carrying little stigma. Those who have worked in the Clondalkin Service know the value of the product, but do not believe that it is unique. The lessons learned are applicable elsewhere.

It is to be hoped that readers of this book will include mental health care professionals, people with mental illnesses, their families and carers and those involved in administration of the mental health services.

This is a good news story which Ireland in 2011 badly needs. Hopefully, it will exhort those who may have been thinking along these lines already to go out and establish something similar for themselves and for the users of mental health services.

3

Radical ideas from Wisconsin

Psychiatry has come far in the last century. The rise of institutional care in the absence of effective treatments gave us the large Victorian asylums which provided refuge for the mentally ill from an unforgiving world around them. The advent of anti-psychotic treatment, while a spectacular breakthrough, did not deliver the expected "cure" for mental illness. Perhaps it was naive to expect they would as mental illness has many and varied causes. All people are different. While home treatment was the expected outcome of the availability of anti-psychotics, it initially failed due to the over-reliance on medication to the detriment of psychological, psychosocial and psycho educational treatments.

Despite the lack of a "magic bullet" the numbers of psychiatric in-patients have been declining steadily worldwide since the mid 1950s. Anti-psychotics are only part of the story. Other factors contributed, including the increase in mental health professionals of all disciplines, mental health legislation, and the growth of the community psychiatric movement.

The concept of community psychiatry originated in the U.S. It was largely shaped by government policy which placed an emphasis on treating those with mental illness in the community as opposed to hospital. The Irish-American President, John Fitzgerald Kennedy, led congress in passing "The Community Mental Health Centres Act" which provided funds for the construction of community mental health centres with specified catchment areas. The idea of defined catchment areas allowing mental health teams to work within geographically confined areas remains a basic principle in the delivery of community mental health care. "Community treatment" is defined as any treatment which takes place in the community in lieu of hospitalisation, following early discharge or after hospitalisation.

The first randomised control study looking at community treatment was Pasamanick et al in 1964.[1] It demonstrated that it was possible to treat people with schizophrenia at home. The study acknowledged the need for a more comprehensive programme for their patient group. It paved the way for the Stein and Test[2] landmark study in 1980. This randomised control trial examined the use of intensive community treatment as an alternative to hospital admission. It adopted broad inclusion criteria allowing the inclusion of some violent and suicidal patients. The results were dramatic. During the five month research study, the community group experienced significantly reduced periods of hospitalisation. A follow up study demonstrated the economic benefit in terms of reduced inpatient costs.

The significance of Stein's and Test's work cannot be overstated. Their "Program of Assertive Community Treatment" (PACT) was groundbreaking. It lead to a transformation in the treatment of those with serious mental illness. It would not be an exaggeration to say it was at least as significant as antipsychotics in reducing dependence on asylums. Anti-psychotics deliver relief from recognisable symptoms of mental ill health. However, community treatment addresses the most common symptom, lack of insight, on a practical level by delivering medication on a daily basis if necessary and on a cognitive level by educating service users and their carers on the benefits of treatment.

---

1   Pasamanick et al. Home vs hospital care for schizophrenics. JAMA 1964: 187:177-181
2   Stein and Test. Alternative to mental hospital treatment: 1. Conceptual model, treatment program and clinical evaluation. Arch Gen Psychiatry 1980;37:392-397

A key factor in delivering care in the community is utilising the skills of a range of mental health professionals. In fact, the "Program of Assertive Community Treatment" as recorded by Stein and Test was the result of a multidisciplinary research group. Mary Ann Test was a psychologist and Leonard Stein was a psychiatrist. They began working together in a research ward of the Mendota State Hospital in Madison, Wisconsin in the late '60s. They were charged with finding ways of helping those with chronic mental illness leave hospital and remain in the community. Their initial efforts were unsuccessful. Test, in an article chronicling the origins of PACT,[3] describes a poorly attended staff meeting in April 1970 where the team expressed their disappointment that "successful" discharges that were carefully linked to existing aftercare services spent relatively short periods of time living in the community and tended to return to the hospital, acutely unwell. At some point, one of the team remarked that "the patients Barb Lontz works with intensively don't come back". Barb Lontz was a social worker who took a "hands on" approach to her clients' discharge. As the team listed her clients it quickly became apparent that most of them remained in the community. Further discussion that evening resulted in the conclusion by a team member that "the community not the hospital is where our patients need the most help" That meeting ended in high spirits.

The next team meeting lasted four hours. The team decided to change the accepted philosophy of care for mental illness at that time. Instead of hospitalisation as the "main event" they decided to make the community the primary locus of treatment. In 1972, the vision became a reality, the research ward was closed and the staff moved to the community to work out of a small office in downtown Madison. The team correctly reasoned their treatment could support those about to be hospitalised and stabilise them thus avoiding admission. This story conceived, developed and ultimately researched by a number of multidisciplinary mental health professionals working together has

---

3 The Origins of PACT as told by Mary Ann Test. The Journal Volume 9 Issue 1 1998

been replicated worldwide. Who could have imagined the effect these "radical ideas" from Wisconsin in the early seventies would have in Ireland? In just under 20 years Clondalkin Mental Health made their move from St. Loman's to the heart of Clondalkin village.

4

We're on our way

Angela (not her real name) is a strong, funny, outgoing, positive woman. She laughs a lot and has a fund of witticisms. She does voluntary work, goes out socialising with her friends once a week, and, according to those who are close to her, is always ready with a helping hand, no matter how busy she is or how difficult her own situation.

She brushes aside with a smile the kind of trouble which would make most of us verge on despair. She doesn't wish to go into it or dwell on it but let's say she is not a stranger to physical ill-health in her dearly loved family and the huge trauma that this can cause.

This, she admits, has taken courage and tenacity and I reckon she has both in spades.

"Despite what had happened to us, we were managing fairly well. My daughter, Jean (not her real name) was working. She was a great kid and we were close.

"She had been a very quiet child and we all loved her. Her grandfather idolised her and would cycle from his own home every day to see her. He had to be stopped from buying her too many presents.

"Then about six years ago she started going a bit weird. She came home one night and told me that somebody at work had given her a bag of money to mind. Then she was afraid a man was watching the house and she thought he might be trying to steal the money. The next thing she told me was that EMINEM wanted her to baby sit.

"I brought her to the GP who said she was not well. Then she vanished which was terrible. She came back after a few days but from there on things went really downhill. She slept all day and was up all night (and of course when she was up, I was up and I still had to be up and doing the next day)

"She still looked like a model but you should have seen her room, it was absolutely manky and she would do nothing to clear it up.

"About this time also, she became addicted to non prescription painkillers. She lost so much weight that she looked like somebody out of a concentration camp and she began to let herself go. She had beautiful long hair and it got so dirty and tangled that I had to cut it off for her.

"One day she threw a glass at me. It just missed me and she said 'I'm going off to the shops and if anybody looks at me I'll f*****g kill them.'

"Things went on like that for a time. Then one day she came to be sobbing and begging me to help her. She said she heard voices in her brain.

"I told her to tell the voices to feck off," Angela laughs reminiscently.

Then her voice breaks "My beautiful daughter, I was so afraid these voices would tell her to do something bad.

"I rang the girls in the Clondalkin Mental Health Centre. They were just brilliant. They came and took her out of the house and got her into Tallaght for a while. Then she came home and went to the Day Hospital and the Phoenix Club.

"It's a good few years on now and she is good at the moment. She gets a monthly injection, she looks after herself again and looks great. She's going to College and next will be a work placement.

"Jean is the best in the world. Her spirit of generosity is amazing I feel so sorry for her that in the years when she was ill, she missed out on friends and possibly marriage.

"The people in the Centre are a godsend. They are just wonderful. In the few days before she gets her next monthly injection you can see the effects of the last one wearing off and she can become a bit agitated.

"She knows and I know that we can ring James or anybody else at the Centre and this is really a great help. I am so much better off myself knowing that I can contact them if things go wrong, that there is always someone here, that I can contact a doctor if necessary and that it is even open for emergencies on Sunday.

Angela's tears are dried and she is bubbling again. "We still have a long way to go, but we're on our way."

5

Models, fidelity and principles

One of the functions of this book is to act as a pointer to mental health services contemplating a more structured and comprehensive move towards a community-based services.

In the preparation process for such a move, the initial emphasis is naturally on what has been done and what has worked well before. The literature must be scoured and the evidence base assembled.

Comprehensive proposals need to be prepared and need to provide a solid rationale for the venture. Projections must be made in the following areas:

- type and location of premises required
- staffing
- population served
- types of diagnoses within that population
- costings
- the effect of the project on the overall quality of care for the targeted population
- what would be the effect on the hospitalisation rate

- will the community object
- what type of training will be required

All these and many other matters have to be taken into consideration. It would be impossible to provide estimations without regard to what has happened and been done before.

The evolution of treatment systems is largely a derivative process, at least initially. Services are developed in certain ways because of local and political factors. For example, the "great confinement" of the 18th and 19th centuries coincided with the rapid economic growth in developed countries with the attendant rise in the population of cities. The behaviours and eccentricities of the mentally ill were less easily contained in cheek by jowl communities where social order was now becoming more important.

Similarly, the great de-confinement or de-institutionalisation movement of the 1960s coincided with the development of the first proven anti-psychotic medication, chlorpromazine, but was also a result of the liberalisation of the 1960s and the "anything goes" philosophy.

It was in this context that the landmark innovative study of Stein and Test took place and gave rise to the first of the major "Models" in this area of treatment.

Great emphasis was now being placed on rehabilitation techniques and modalities to prepare patients with long-term mental illness for re-integration into the community. These techniques were assiduously studied and their effects measured. However, no matter how good the preparatory work in the hospital, almost inevitably, discharged patients returned within months, often psychotic and dishevelled.

As is often the case, out of complete frustration and low morale, a new approach was mooted. This approach was almost Darwinian in its evolution. A particular social worker at the Mendota State Hospital in Wisconsin, (who fortuitively was particularly conscientious) found a way to block the "revolving door". Her patients did not require re-admission. The secret of her success was in providing in-vivo training and support to discharged individuals in all aspects of their new community challenges. Thus, the concept was born. The kernel of the insight was that "place, train and support" was far more effective than "train, place and don't support". Previous logic was turned on its head and it was stated, "Some patients are too sick to be treated or rehabilitated in hospital".

In order to measure the effects of any new treatment, it has to be operationalised into an easily recognisable and separate items much like the new model of car. It had to have certain definable characteristics if the efficacy or effectiveness of this model was to be compared with treatment as usual or other forms of treatment.

Excellent results arising out of the implementation of a particular model in a particular set of circumstances or locations, also have to be generalisable. In other words, this package has to be applied in other locations and in different settings for the wisdom of its approach to be universally accepted. Testing the validity of the model implies that it has to be implemented faithfully. Thus, the term, fidelity to the model.

The Programme for Assertive Community Treatment (PACT), initially called "Training in Community Living" became the buzzword and hallmark for progressive services throughout the United States in the 1980s and 1990s. This approach was mainly used to rehabilitate long-term hospital residents, but also to treat in the community those who had many frequent hospitalisations or even those with serious illnesses heading in that direction.

Just to show how detailed was that fidelity, it is useful to look at the fidelity check-list published by the NAMI (National Alliance on Mental Illness) Act Technical Assistance Centre. The checklist involves 157 items under the following headings:

- staff composition
- key staff roles
- outreach and continuity of care
- programme size and intensity
- admission and discharge criteria specified
- clinical charts

- office space
- inter-agency relationship
- hours of operation
- team communication and planning
- assessment and treatment planning
- services
- policy and procedure manual

The fidelity of services purporting to be ACT in nature can be audited against these types of checklists and a mini-industry has now developed around this concept.

The Clondalkin Project[4]

In the planning stages for the Clondalkin Project (as it was known at the time) in the late 1980s, the concept of fidelity was not being consistently and rigorously applied.

Dr. Ian Daly was impressed with the Stein and Test papers and approach, but identified certain necessary differences between the culture of a small town near Madison, Wisconsin, and the burgeoning conurbation of Clondalkin.

For example, in Madison, youngsters left home at the age of 17 or 18 to live on their own in apartments. Accordingly, when patients were being rehabilitated, they were placed in single dwelling apartments. In Dublin city at that time, and to a degree still, the tradition was of youngsters continuing to live with their parents until either moving to a new city or getting married. The family at that time was a much more important aspect of individuals' lives and the family, therefore, had to be an intrinsic focus of treatment and support. In that respect, the work of Ian Falloon on family behaviour therapy was incorporated into the Clondalkin Project/Model.

---

4   The models "plundered" in the establishment of the Clondalkin Project are set out
    in more detail in Chapter 9, starting on page 47.

"We were very excited and a bit apprehensive. We wanted very much to succeed. We had put our heads over the parapet, we had got extra resources and we were afraid we mightn't justify people's faith in us, mightn't be able to deliver the kind of service we wanted. Our objective was to treat patients in the community without admitting them to hospital.

"From a social worker's point of view, Clondalkin was a fairly bleak place then. There was high unemployment, real poverty and few services. In winter, you couldn't take off your coat on a home visit because of the cold in the houses. People hadn't jobs or money to heat their homes. They had moved into new communities and were displaced and without support.

"There was barrenness about Clondalkin. The main things you noticed were pylons. There was no Money Advice Bureau (MABS), no family support workers and very little access to home help. We saw a lot of isolation from mainstream society.

"As I said, there was huge unemployment and physical institutionalisation. There was poor public transport, people were away from their old families and friends, they had no money to go to pubs, they watched British TV and bought British newspapers (either because they were cheaper or they related better to them).

"One of the things that became very apparent was the hidden effects on families of mental health illness, it was only by going into the homes and getting to know them and their families in their own place that the full impact of mental illness was evident. Families in my experience generally go to great lengths to care for their people who are ill and they may feel cut off from other family members and support because they are unwilling to share what might be seen as a stigma.

"I developed a special interest in the needs of children being raised by parents who had mental health difficulties. One of the effects of community care was that people with severe mental illness were living in the community, marrying and having children. I was interested to know if parental illness impacted on the children's lives and carried out a research project to look at the effect of severe mental illness on these children. I found there was little difference between them and children of well parents.

"The majority were fine, a small number had quite serious difficulties and a small number were highly self-reliant and very competent at looking after their parent and their family. I remember a 12 year old girl who went into town to buy a first communion outfit for her seven year old brother.

"It is very important when delivering community mental health services for staff to take cognisance of their patients' children and their needs and to be mindful of the effect of medication on parents looking after children.

"Funding was also made available to provide specialist family interventions as it was recognised that to maximise treatments benefits families needed education and training in order that they could improve their coping skills. The team began to educate patients and families in the whole area of mental illness. Some had never even been told their diagnosis and hadn't really questioned it over the previous 10 – 15 years. This education enabled patients and their families to be more in charge of the illness and to access peer support as provided by organisations such as Schizophrenia Ireland, now SHINE.

"We were successful in not admitting patients to hospital. Our belief was that admission should only be for patients who really needed to be there. For others it is a more positive experience to remain at home because it is less disrupting to routine less stigmatising and more importantly, it is more effective for their illness.

"One woman who was coming to our day hospital told me that her children thought she was going to work as usual and this was reassuring to her as they were very upset when she was hospitalised in the past. There was a small number of people who were used to going to hospital for respite and there were difficulties there because we had no alternative for them. But overall, people living in the community had a better quality of life, there was less stigmatism of their illness, they had support and they and their families were much happier.

"Another learning experience for us was the importance of educating our fellow professionals in the community so that they understood what the service could offer as they are often the first port of call for people in difficulties."

Victoria Somers moved from the Clondalkin Project in the mid '90s to work in St. Ita's Hospital Portrane, Co. Dublin and subsequently was appointed Principal Mental Health Social Worker in the Kildare Mental Health Services, Naas. She is involved in the Mental Health Social Workers Group that has been seeking to advocate for more multidiscipline team working in the mental health services. She is also a member of the Mental Health Commission.

14

The reality of their lives
An interview with Dr. Fiona Keogh

To get a chance to return to Ireland as a researcher with an innovative new mental health project was a great opportunity for Irish born Fiona Keogh. It was late 1989, she was 24 years old, just three years out of college and Irish Health Boards did not employ researchers. It was a first for the Eastern Health Board, which had just recruited her – there wasn't even a pay scale for this type of work.

Fiona had graduated from Trinity College Dublin as a psychologist in 1986 and gone to England to work as a Medical Information Officer for the West Essex Health Authority, based in Harlow. While working in the public health department there, she became involved in a pilot site for the national breast screening programme. Part of Fiona's job was to target a message which would reach all eligible women in the area. She was then seconded to the roll out of the national breast screening programme for women in the North East Thames Regional Health Authority, which had a population of about three million people.

When she joined the Clondalkin Mental Health Project, she first got an office in the Nurses' Home in St. Loman's but quickly moved into Ballydowd House where the project was based.

"I knew nothing about the mental health services so I didn't see anything unusual about the service in St. Loman's at that time. I see now that it was very different – it wasn't a Victorian gothic building and everybody seemed to be more open to new ways of working than in many of the psychiatric facilities I subsequently visited. For me, it was an exciting new job and a great opportunity to be involved in researching an innovative new service."

An important part of the new project was to evaluate it. Under the direction of Dr. Ian Daly, Fiona worked on the research design and identified the measures to be used in evaluating the new service. "I was very much a junior researcher being guided by Ian who had a great research orientation. I wasn't a clinical psychologist and had no clinical experience, so one of the first tasks was to train in clinical interviewing. I went to a course in Cork to train in the Present State Examination (PSE)."

The research was designed to evaluate the effectiveness of the new service for patients and their families and to compare it with the neighbouring Tallaght sector, which did not have the new elements of the service.

Up to then most studies had compared new models of service with traditional forms of care which focused on hospital admission. "Even before the start of the project in Clondalkin, St. Loman's was different. It had a strong community orientation with Outpatient Clinics and Community Psychiatry Nurses and a lower than average use of inpatient admission."

This research was novel at the time in that a new model of service was being compared to the next best model – not just standard inpatient care. The Tallaght sector was part of the overall St. Loman's catchment area and also had a strong community orientation. In research terms this meant it would be more difficult to demonstrate large differences in outcomes and was a robust test of the new model of service.

The aim of the research was to evaluate this new model of community mental health service which included home care and day hospital treatment as alternatives to hospitalisation. We wanted to determine the effectiveness of this model for long-term and new or acute patients, on a range of outcomes. The main outcomes examined how patients were doing clinically, socially and the experience of families. We also recorded all the services used by patients to see if service use increased or decreased as a result of their treatment. A model which reduced hospital admissions at the cost of hugely increased use in other parts of the service could not be deemed effective."

One of the key outcomes was 'family burden'; the experience of families of living with a member with mental ill health. This was of particular interest because many of the concerns about the Clondalkin model were that acutely ill people would not be in hospital but would be at home with their families and that this might increase their burden and distress. For this reason a family member of each patient was also interviewed where possible.

A random sample of 150 long-term patients was selected, 75 from Clondalkin and 75 from Tallaght. In addition, 150 consecutive new referrals were included in the research, 75 from Clondalkin and 75 from Tallaght. A total of 297 patients were eventually interviewed for the research. Of these 297 patients, 200 had family members who were available or agreed to be interviewed.

"I started with the longer term patients. I couldn't have done this without the two community psychiatric nurses working in the area, Sylvia Divelly and Geraldine McKenna. They were wonderful, very committed to supporting patients and very helpful with the research. The two CPNs in Tallaght, Dermot and Breda, were also wonderfully supportive. The CPNs introduced me to the patients and I arranged a time to meet and interview them.

"This large sample of 297 patients enabled us to compare outcomes for different groups of patients and people with different diagnoses. Each patient and family member was interviewed 18 months after their first interview to measure any changes that occurred between interviews. This enabled us to determine the effectiveness of the new model."

Fiona did most of her interviews in the patients' homes. "It was one of the most valuable experiences of my life. Seeing people in their own homes was very important to get an idea of the reality of their lives. The experience has influenced my thinking ever since. To see the poverty of many – what it looked like, what it felt like to be in houses with no heating – made a lasting impression." At that time unemployment was very high in these areas, about 20 per cent in Clondalkin and Tallaght.

"But the people were great, warm, genuine and co-operative. There was always a cup of tea and 99 per cent of people welcomed me into their homes – the ones who didn't were generally not well at the time."

Fiona worked with the ESRI which inputted the huge amount of data she collected.

The key findings were that patients in the Clondalkin service had reduced hospital admissions and those who were admitted were in hospital for shorter periods. Crucially, this decrease in the use of inpatient admission did not lead to an increase in family burden. In fact the burden on their families decreased. The large reduction in hospital use meant that the Clondalkin model was a cost effective way of delivering mental health services. Patients and families were also satisfied with this model of care.

"Clinically there was no great difference between the outcomes for people in the two services, but then it is unusual in research like this to see a major clinical difference. What was important was that people did not get worse clinically and did better in other areas of their lives, as did their families."

The results were publicised at a series of conferences with international speakers, including Dr. Leonard Stein from Wisconsin and Dr. Joe Connolly from the Maudsley in London.

If this could be done in the St. Loman's area – then the largest and one of the most deprived catchment areas in the country – it could be done elsewhere. This model of service is now recommended in the national policy A Vision for Change.

For Fiona Keogh, it was the foundation of her career giving her a breadth of exposure in designing and running such a large scale study from scratch. The research formed the basis for her PhD.

She spent three and a half years in the service and went on to work in the Mental Health Division of the Health Research Board.

Dr Fiona Keogh is now a research consultant and has worked with the senior management team in the Mental Health Commission to implement the Mental Health Act and with the Expert Group on Mental Health Policy to write up A Vision for Change. Much of the thinking in A Vision for Change reflects a direct link to work done by the Clondalkin project.

15

Driving your uncle's Rolls Royce
By Dr Pat Devitt

I became interested in home care in the mid 1980s, when the whole concept was gaining ground in Ireland. At that time, I was a member of the former Eastern Health Board and of its Special Hospitals' Committee, where the Programme Manager, Michael Walsh was talking about Faloon and his new home care initiative in the U.K.

Around that time, I went to Buckingham where I attended an open day by Falloon. I was impressed when he said that when people had a crisis, the mental health team would descend and provide a full wrap-'round support service including shopping, cooking and cleaning in people's homes.

Some time later, in the United States, I was part of an interview board for a post of Director of Nursing and – perhaps provocatively – I asked a candidate if she would go out and do the shopping, if one of her patients in the community had a crisis. She said she certainly would not – she was a nurse. For me, it was the wrong answer!

When I was in the US in the late '90s, home care had become very popular – the idea was that people with mental illness should have as much autonomy as possible. It was realised that when people went into institutions their expectations of themselves were lower and after a while they got to the stage that they were being treated like children. People act according to their expectations of themselves and indeed of the expectations of people around them. I used to be very surprised when I visited patients with long term mental illnesses who had been admitted to a general hospital and found you couldn't see any obvious signs of their mental illness, although it would have been very pronounced when they were in the psychiatric hospital. Prolonged psychiatric hospitalisation has this effect on peoples' perceptions of themselves and their future.

I remember in the mid-1990s in Syracuse, New York, USA, hearing the term "fidelity to the model" for the first time. This was in the context of a grant from the New York State government to the local county mental health service to set up an Assertive Community Treatment or ACT Team. The conditions for the grant funding were quite clear. The project had to be designed and operated with the utmost fidelity to the original model.

When I came back to Ireland, I knew about Ian Daly and the Clondalkin Project. I got a job as consultant psychiatrist in St. Loman's Hospital/Tallaght service. When Dr. Ian Daly became Clinical Director on the retirement of Dr. Dermot Walsh, he made the very wise decision to give up clinical practice and concentrate on his Clinical Director work. At that time, Clondalkin had grown and should really have had two consultants, but Ian had a senior registrar and three registrars, so the senior registrar was essentially acting as a junior consultant.

When Ian offered me the Clondalkin post, I viewed it with some trepidation. It was a bit like being asked to drive your uncle's Rolls Royce – you'd be afraid you might crash it or damage it in some way. The Clondalkin Project was the Rolls Royce of the mental health service and had been copied in Monaghan and Cavan.

I remember very well when I went to work the first day, there was a round-room meeting with about 20 people, including the staff of the day hospital. There were doctors, nurses, people working in psychology, social work, occupational therapy and of course students flocking all over the place – and I'm sure they all wanted to know what this consultant who was taking over from Ian was like.

I can still remember some of the cases which we worked on at that meeting. There was a man who was receiving Clozapine. from the nurses at home. He didn't always take it, the house was a bit chaotic and they were concerned that the children might pick up the medication. In addition, the man had a reputation for violence. It brought it home to me how difficult it was to provide home care in deprived areas. My respect for the team was immense. This was the type of patient with whom they were dealing.

Another memory was of a patient discharged following a short admission. She had locked herself into her home and wouldn't come out and there were fears she might harm the children. We all went out to the house, where the nurses were really excellent and she agreed to come out and on down to the day hospital.

Soon, it became obvious to me what a very good team spirit and sense of purpose there was among those working on the project. As I said, it was the Rolls Royce of the mental health services and staff were perceived as being the elite of the services.

There was a research project going on comparing the outcomes from home care and day-hospital care. This was quite stressful for home care staff as at that time they were providing home care for the entire catchment area including Ballyfermot and Tallaght. Unfortunately, it had to be abandoned because it was logistically impossible for the nurses to travel all around. It could be re-started now that home care is provided in all the sectors of the catchment area.

The basic principle of the service was that patients, in general, even with very serious illness, received better treatment in the community than in hospital.

Our concern was to prevent or reduce the length of stay in hospital of patients who were seriously mentally ill. We tried to prevent admission by assessing people, treating them in the day hospital and in their homes – sometimes heroically.

Interestingly, there wasn't any practical divide between acute care and long-term care (as found in models of home care and assertive outreach). Patients' needs were just met and in their own environment—in the community.

I remember one Christmas there was a patient with bipolar disorder and the family virtually "specialled" that patient over the Christmas with the assistance of our staff who were on duty. The patient got through it and the family were delighted. They would have considered it stigmatising if the patient had been admitted to hospital.

We also treated patients with personality disorders especially those who had frequent emergency admissions. We knew that hospital stay, particularly long hospital stay, was not good for them. They tended to turn up on Friday evening, perhaps cutting themselves and threatening suicide. We wanted to see if the home care team could have a useful role in reducing the chaos of their lives and the chaos they caused in the community.

Gradually we started laying down rules. Where we would not admit patients to hospital we would, however, deal with them as intensively as possible through the day hospital and home care. As a result, staff became very expert in treating these patients. We set up mini teams consisting of a nurse, a psychologist and an occupational therapist to look after some particularly chaotic patients. There was the woman who would wander into other people's houses and call ambulances day and night when she was depressed. She was causing chaos in the community.

We found it very productive to reduce medication, to take away all unused medication and, if necessary, maintain patients on one medication. We found low doses of depot anti-psychotic medication especially helpful with this group. This, of course, meant that there was regular follow-up with the community nurses which kept matters in check and alerted us to any signs of relapse. It was fairly unique, I think, how we managed these patients with personality disorders. We even submitted plans for a catchment-wide service along these lines.

We had two full meetings of the entire team each week, which everyone attended. There was no cross referral between the disciplines, if a need arose, someone volunteered to meet it – this was one of the key aspects of the service.

Another key issue was that there was no formal division between the day hospital, the day centre and the nurses, psychologists and others who worked in the community. Everybody became more generic as time went on. There was fluidity in the movement of patients and staff between the day hospital and the home care service.

Surprisingly for me, there was very little tension between such disparate groups. There was also a very welcoming attitude and in general the place was over-run with students because its training reputation had got around.

At the meetings we frequently went back to first principles and what our mission was and we found the answer to many difficulties there. Our mission was to provide a comprehensive community-based psychiatric service caring for the seriously mentally ill and an assessment service for patients referred by GPs. Everyone knew exactly that the type of

Christmas lunch 2004 — *Dr Pat Devitt and Team*

patients we were treating were seriously ill and by treating them in the community we preserved their autonomy and ensured a better outcome.

If a GP referred a patient with mild illness to us, we did an assessment and then referred the patient back to the GP.

Our outpatient clinic operated by the motto: The Three Ss – Screening, Serious illness and Stability. If we detected instability, then we immediately provided the appropriate level of services, either in the day hospital or at home and then discussed their future plan of care at the meeting the following day.

I was very impressed at how the day hospital functioned as a very acute hospital, yet it was in a very small room. There was an expectation

Vincent Monaghan, Rosaleen Molloy, Michael Buckley, Margaret Downey, Anne Horan, Mary McGlynn, Margaret Lambert, Eamon Kenny, Kathleen O'Sullivan

that serious illness would be treated and the patient would then go on to another aspect of care. In our day care services we would collect acutely ill patients and send them home by taxi. At the day hospital, they would receive treatment and a midday meal.

I used to point out to patients who said they did not want to be discharged to a day hospital that in fact they would get more intensive interventions than as an inpatient and they could sleep in their own beds at night. It was helpful that families, who might have been a bit anxious initially about their son, daughter, husband or wife being discharged to a day hospital, preferred it when they tried it out.

Once patients and families settled into this type of care, there was no expectation that whenever a blip occurred they would be admitted to hospital. The first port of call would be the day hospital and we encouraged drop-in for known patients.

We were not set up for patients whose primary problems were drug or alcohol addiction. We were aware that some people would like us to take everyone in but these patients didn't mix very well with patients with more mainstream illnesses, so we referred them appropriately.

Another area where we had considerable success was in treating post natal depression, as this was particularly suited to home care. A new mother, in a crisis, might pose a risk to herself and her baby and in cases of prolonged depression it might cause a problem with bonding.

Our staff developed a great expertise in providing home education for family members such as husbands and Grannies as well as offering support to the mothers. The mothers were often referred to and brought along to a variety of mainstream community supports.

With all these services and support we achieved one of the lowest admission rates in the country thanks to the broad shoulders of the team and the patients and families involved.

There was of course the risk of violence, so we developed the Risk of Violence Assessment (ROVA) instrument (a 2-page, 1-leaf pink form). We were very conscious of risk but rather than be frightened and cowed by it we worked out how to manage it. After all, low admissions were all about safe ways to manage risk. Our risk management was better because it was an intrinsic part of our work.

Our focus was not on prevention of suicide but on treating the underlying distress. We recongised that many suicide threats are manipulative but the threat could disappear if we could effectively support them until the acute distress was alleviated or disappeared. It must also be remembered that the early days of hospital admission are a time of suicide risk, Instead we offered a range of services. We were not always successful. In my time, there were three tragic suicides but interestingly the families never blamed us. We had close and on-going contact with these families and at least one of them told us how grateful they were for the work we had done and the help we had provided to the patient who died. Of course we reviewed these suicides at team meetings and tried to establish if we could have prevented them if we had done things differently.

Looking back, the people who worked in the service in my time were truly heroic – Queen Maeve and Granuaile kind of women and wonderful men. They were strong and compassionate but wouldn't put up with any messing and their judgment was impeccable. I would always direct junior doctors. to consult with them before making any difficult decisions. This gave the junior doctors the great support of working in a team.

The staff were the bedrock of the service and that remained a given, despite staff movement. And there was a lot of movement because people wanted to get it on their CV that they had worked in Clondalkin and then they moved on. I think that what happened was that those who stayed provided stability which was then blended with the innovation which the new people brought in. So, while people came and went, the ship remained steady.

Some people were, of course really nervous about risks but they were guided and supported by the team and then they developed their own autonomy and instead of being scared they began to enjoy it.

If I were to summarise what made Clondalkin work so well, I think I would have to stress the close well-functioning team with emphasis on generic working, the lack of internal referrals, the sense of clear purpose and commitment, the management of risk, the commitment to family support and, most important, the common-sense pragmatism, heroism and flexibility of the staff.

Dr. Pat Devitt, Inspector of Mental Hospitals and Consultant Psychiatrist, Clondalkin Project May 2001 – May 2008

16

Over Molloy's off-licence
By Dr Marina Bowe

While I was doing my basic psychiatric training in St. Patrick's Hospital as part of the Dublin University scheme, I had heard a lot about community psychiatry in Clondalkin, in the Dublin West/South West Psychiatric Service. This was something about which I had no previous experience and I applied for a placement there. I didn't get it but I got a post in Liaison Psychiatry based in Tallaght hospital, where I quickly became so aware of how effective community services were.

I could contact the homecare team, either during the week or at weekends, and this enabled us to cut down on admissions of people who would previously have been admitted to hospital in-patients.

When I went on to higher training, I was determined to get a senior registrar post in the Tallaght service for a year and work in Clondalkin because of what I had seen of their ability to reduce admissions by treating people at home. I didn't want to finish my training without this experience and it became the goal of my higher training. The Clondalkin project had been underway for about 18 years at that time and was the only community team in the country which was fully staffed by all disciplines.

I started off my higher training in the Dundalk sector of the HSE North East in October 2006 and then in July 2007, I got a job as a senior registrar in the Clondalkin service. I spent a year working with the team in Clondalkin which was just fantastic. What was being done there was best practice internationally and I always thought that if you hadn't worked in a place like this and seen how it operated, you wouldn't be able to bring this type of experience to your work and your career.

Going to Clondalkin, I had really high expectations, as I saw this as the Rolls Royce of the mental health services. The first morning I rang up for directions, I was fairly surprised when I was told it was over Molloy's off-licence! I didn't think you could have this unique health

Margaret Downey and Vincent Monaghan opening up in October 2010

service above an off-licence. Then I arrived and was met by the team, who were all having tea! My next shock was my office, which was like a cubby hole – and one I had to share into the bargain!

I just didn't know how the system worked. Rather quickly, I realised that the morning and evening tea breaks were the hub of the service – the day's work was allocated in the morning and reviewed in the evening. If I left my office (and indeed if I stayed in it), I met staff and patients which, of course, was the whole idea.

The centre was very cramped but again that was helpful because it resulted in continual brainstorming as people met and re-met. In Clondalkin there was more brainstorming than in any other team I knew. There were no silos, everybody was encouraged to give their views and work outside their comfort zones.

I had another surprise the first morning when this very unwell girl continually barged into my office and basically tried to wreck it. I said to the senior nurse "Shouldn't we admit her?" She laughed and said "she'll be fine, We'll just monitor her and stabilise her on medication." Her Dad arrived later and he was very annoyed that we hadn't admitted her – but that wasn't the way it worked in Clondalkin.

At that time, we didn't have many patients, but the ones we had were very sick. Everyone was reviewed on a daily basis, so we knew exactly how they were doing. My job was to stabilise the patients and I learned rapidly that this service was better than any hospital admission. Here they were assessed on a daily basis and their medication supervised, exactly as it would have been if they were in hospital.

After a few weeks I learned that the girl whom I had met the first day had indeed got better with a combination of day hospital/home care and both she and her family were very grateful to have avoided a lengthy hospital admission that would have meant removing her from the community, most likely against her will and would have been quite stigmatising. It would also have been much harder for her to go back to her community and to work, if she had been away in hospital.

When she was better and back to work, the team continued to follow her up to find out what she would like to do with her life – would she like extra training or had she special interests she would like to pursue.. The great idea was that they wanted to return her to full functioning as quickly as possible.

Basically, families took a large amount of responsibility for the home care of patients, supervising medication and learning to live with the illness when the patient was unwell. Previously the family would have virtually abrogated responsibility for the patient, who would be in hospital. Here they were involved, indeed sometimes over-involved.

The other area in which they were very strong was in the education of the patients' families. People with major mental illness do worse in stressed environments. The team used home care to educate families and give them hope. It was asking families to take on a lot but in doing that you helped and supported them. You were also able to educate them about early warning symptoms and advise them to contact the service if and when they noticed them. In theory this is what every service should be doing, of course, but Clondalkin was doing it.

It was almost informal, you'd be meeting patients all the time, in the centre sometimes over a cup of tea and believe me you get to know a person much better and can do a much better assessment over a cup of tea rather than in a formal environment. Of course, we did formal assessments also, but that was only part of the work. The Home Care team took a very informal approach to patients. They called to see them at home, brought them out for coffee or lunch, to the cinema or to play snooker, which was a real breakthrough for people who never left home. They were out – with the security of a health professional if they panicked – and they learned that they could do it.

Then there was the A1 Club, where younger people with mental illness were encouraged to socialise or go on outings. It was wonderful when a group of them went out and they looked no different from any other group.

The Clondalkin staff always worked outside the box and were hugely involved. Nothing was too much for them. Nurses would go out and pick up shopping or clean up a house if necessary. Their motto was "Go in and do."

For example a lot of anti psychotic drugs cause weight gain. There was dietary advice but our team took it further and ran a walking group which not only was socially beneficial but the exercise countered the effect of the medication.

Then everything was helped because there were no paper referrals. If you have to fill out a referral form it can be quite off putting and you are inclined to tick boxes. But if you're doing it face to face you have to think what you are asking your colleagues to do. Face to face, it is easier to provide all the knowledge you have and your colleagues can tell you what they think they can or cannot do, which is much more effective and faster than having to make a referral and waiting for a report back. Of course there are people who will say if there is no paper referral there is no proof you ever made a referral. That wasn't a problem. If somebody said they would do something in Clondalkin, they did it.

When Dr. Pat Devitt was heading up the service, he put a lot of trust and responsibility in people. If he thought they knew their jobs he would encourage them to work outside the box, he gave them trust and responsibility. This worked really well because everyone had confidence to initiate. Everybody was listened to including visiting students, everybody got an equal chance to have their say at meetings.

However, there was no doubt but that Pat was the boss and the team leader. Ultimately he was the person who took the final decision, when decisions were needed.

For me it was a great experience. I got clinical knowledge but also learned how to manage a service. I was also very lucky because while I was there I got an opportunity to act up and be in charge, be accountable and see how I managed it.

In Clondalkin there was an enthusiasm among staff. They were so committed to what they were doing. They believed there was a better way – to keep people out of hospital and give them back their lives.

They built relationships with their patients that I had not seen to that extent anywhere else and they seemed to gain their trust, so that patients would tell staff they didn't like taking medication, rather than just giving it up and getting sick. They managed all this without being intrusive. They weren't buddies they were still professional, but they kept people well and prevented relapses. It might be the 'phone call or the visit but patients kept on getting care and of course the families knew they could contact staff if they had any worries. The "open door" policy encouraged patients and families to make contact with their key worker if they had a problem. They were told to ring if they thought something was wrong.

This of course, meant you could never plan your day as you could be told that somebody had rung and wasn't well and you would need to see that patient immediately. That also happened with emergency referrals from GPs or Emergency Departments. We aimed to provide a same day review. If a GP said someone was ill and he or she was sending them to hospital, our response would be to tell them to send them to us instead. We would try to avoid a hospital admission if the patient could be managed in the day hospital or with home care.

I got all this experience and knowledge and I wanted to share it. All sector teams in the St Loman's sector provide similar services to Clondalkin. I thought if it could be done in Dublin West/South West, it could be done anywhere and I was disappointed that things were not changing everywhere.

I feel that it is an inequality in the health service that your address determines the kind of psychiatric care you get – it is nearly worse than the public/ private divide in the general health services. Because of all this I never louse an opportunity to spread the Clondalkin message.

While I was in Clondalkin we had a lot of visiting teams, so we put together a PowerPoint presentation to explain what we were doing. This got such a great reaction that I floated the idea of an Open Day This had already been mooted on a number of occasions before but not followed through. This time it happened and over 50 people from all over the country came to a meeting in one of the local schools. We presented our work and experience. Each discipline spoke about their jobs. The feedback was extremely positive – and out of that open day came the idea for this book –

Dr. Marina Bowe, Senior Registrar, Clondalkin Mental Health July 2007-July 2008

17

Where we go from here
By Dr Finian Kelly

The Clondalkin Project was already known to me as a significant innovation in Irish psychiatry when I started to work as a consultant psychiatrist in the Dublin West/South West Psychiatric Service (which covers Crumlin, Clondalkin, Ballyfermot, Lucan and Tallaght) in 2003. At that time, I was working in the Ballyfermot/Lucan sector which is adjacent to Clondalkin, and the consultants for the two sectors often shared issues and discussed service innovations – what we now call peer support.

When Dr. Pat Devitt, who was the consultant psychiatrist in Clondalkin, was appointed Inspector of Mental Hospitals in 2008, the Dublin West/South West Clinical Director, Dr. Ian Daly asked me to move over to Clondalkin, which I did in June 2008.

What I took over was a really well functioning community psychiatric team. The staff believed in and was dedicated to community treatment, with use of in-patient hospital care only when absolutely necessary. It was a cohesive, multidisciplinary team that worked seamlessly together, unlike any other multidisciplinary team I had previously experienced.

It was a team where people were open to each other's ideas, challenges, diagnoses and treatment plans. Nobody was offended if their ideas were questioned, open discussion was the norm. It was also a team where people readily volunteering to take on cases, often the difficult ones. The team was open to innovation and to bringing new ideas into the way the team functioned.

An example of this innovation was when we discussed the concept of the multi-disciplinary team doing the initial patient assessment, which traditionally had been the preserve of the doctors on the team. I arranged a training session to facilitate this and expected four or five people to turn up – instead 18 of the 22 members of the team attended.

Another impressive new development was the "Stay Well" group for young people with early psychotic illness. This was the team's response to their recognition that rehabilitation towards recovery begins immediately after a first psychotic episode. This treatment group was researched and established with a minimum of funding and external training, the team members themselves doing the background research and learning in order to establish the group. What they have effectively established is a programme that follows the principles of best practice for the treatment of first episode psychosis.

Another striking thing about the team is that they work so closely with the families and carers of patients. There is a strong emphasis on educating patients and families about mental illness, relapse risks and the need to be alert to early symptoms of relapse. The trust that is built up means that patients, and their families and carers, feel able to seek advice and treatment early on if there are any signs of relapse.

A seemingly small thing that makes a huge difference in the way the team functions is that there are no paper referrals and no waiting lists among the different disciplines. All acute patients are openly discussed at the twice weekly multidisciplinary team meetings, which is where the referral process happens – there is a verbal referral and the only documentation necessary is in the meeting minutes.

The Clondalkin team's use of community resources is also very impressive. The Clondalkin Project is dedicated to and resourced mainly for treatment of the serious, enduring mental illnesses. Fortunately Clondalkin has great community resources, including excellent counselling services such as Beacon of Light and Pieta house. We use these services frequently, often directing patients to them. There is a great interaction between the team and these local community resources. We have been building, and will continue to build, strong links and even partnerships with these community services.

I am now looking to the future. There is a long-standing plan to move to new premises, a recognition that the Mental Health Centre in which the service is currently housed is a less than ideal building. There are plans to move into a premises shared with Primary Care teams. This new premises will allow us to have the Day Hospital, Day Centre and outpatient clinics all operating from the same building. It will facilitate improved links with primary care.

There is going to be a need for a second consultant in the not too distant future, given that the population is burgeoning to over 60,000. At present, the medical members of the team consist of one consultant, one senior registrar, two registrars and a GP trainee. We have about 850 patients treated by our service every year and our referral rate has increased in 2010, which may be due to people's current economic problems.

Another aim is to focus on the earlier identification and treatment of people with serious mental illness. We need to develop comprehensive treatment plans for patients and their families, not just the standard medical treatments, but the greater area of recovery, in areas of resocialisation and getting back into occupation or education. We need to develop treatment programmes that take into account all the social and physical problems that accompany serious psychiatric illness, and implement these programmes of treatment right in the early stages of treatment.

We will be working increasingly with community resources. Already, members of the team are participating in various community activities, such as the Clondalkin Action on Suicide in North Clondalkin.

I am involved in the pre-planning group for the Jigsaw project. Jigsaw is an initiative to identify mental health needs and provide appropriate intervention for young people in the 12 – 25 age group. Jigsaw projects are already in operation in Ballymun and Galway and pre-Jigsaw planning is now underway in Clondalkin. This is being supported on an advisory level by Headstrong at the moment and it is hoped that the Clondalkin Jigsaw project will ultimately be financially supported by Headstrong.

As part of this planning, a needs analysis is being done, determining what is needed and what is already provided. This is very relevant to us in the Clondalkin Mental Health Service as in 2009, one third of our new patients, 125 individuals, were aged less than 26 years. The kind of problems these young people have are often significantly distressing psychological problems but may not be serious psychiatric illness as such, and may be more appropriately treated outside of the specialist psychiatric services.

Another area we have to develop is a close working relationship with the drug and alcohol treatment services. Two-thirds of patients referred to us have a problem with drugs and/or alcohol impinging on their psychological symptoms, although drug or alcohol addiction are the primary presentation in only about five per cent of cases. We need to tackle both together, rather than separately. When people have an addiction problem with mental illness, both have to be treated if the outcome is to be positive. If people are using alcohol or drugs, they are more likely to be poorly adherent to treatment and more likely to have symptom recurrence. One of the skills we currently lack is the mental health service is addiction counsellors.

Last year, we began establishing a close working relationship with the Adolescent Mental Health Service. Two new consultants have been appointed to the Tallaght/St. James's Adolescent Mental Health Service and we are working closely with them in the care of people in the 16 – 17 age group. This allows us to become involved early with young people develop- ing serious mental health illnesses like schizophrenia or bipolar disorder.

We are also developing liaison with General Practitioners, which is key to detecting potentially serious illness early on. GPs are very keen to use us a resource to get advice without necessarily having to refer on patients. A number of them would like a forum for advice and members of our multidisciplinary team are currently looking at how we might develop such as service.

Dr. Finian Kelly, Consultant Psychiatrist, Clondalkin Mental Health Project 2008

18

We are all so lucky to have found the clinic

David (not his real name) was a quiet studious lad, who while he was growing up never gave his parents any cause for concern. He was happy in his own company, got on well with his family and was a non-drinker and non-smoker. He went on to take a first class degree and at the age of 28 was a young professional with a good job in a financial business, living in rented accommodation in Dublin.

He had found a modern apartment which he decided to buy and asked his mother if it would be acceptable if he moved back home for a few months to save on the rent.

Maeve (not her real name) and her husband were delighted to welcome him home but within a very short time Maeve was concerned about her son.

"I said to Daddy, 'something's not right'. David keeps saying 'Mammy I'm going to lose my job.' A cousin of mine worked in the same business and I asked him to make enquiries to see if David was in danger of losing his job. He checked it out and came back and told me that David's work was fine and there was no question of his losing his job but they were worried about him at work as they thought there might be something wrong with him.

"I remembered then that about two years earlier, David had told me he was suffering from depression. I should have taken more notice but I didn't and it didn't seem to be affecting him."

David bought his apartment but things began going downhill almost immediately.

"David never wasted money, he had been saving for the apartment and he liked to go on holidays and now that the major part of his savings were gone on the apartment, it appeared that the money had been a safety net for him and he was worried that this safety net was gone.

"He accused family members of trying to harm him and of being in cahoots with criminal gangs to harm him. It was very scary.

"Daddy brought him to the A & E in Tallaght but they said he was no danger to others or himself and indeed he wasn't. He was always a quiet non-aggressive lad but he was very unwell, he was getting worse and we didn't know what to do.

"I took him to my own doctor about 13 months ago and at this stage he had himself so worn out and exhausted that he fell asleep in the waiting room. The doctor asked him if he would go to Naas Hospital and he agreed. He was there for four or five days, but he didn't do well there and they got nowhere with him. He didn't want anybody to visit but me. I took my mother in once and he got very upset and embarrassed.

"When I arrived to visit him in Naas one day I found he wasn't in his room. They told me he was being transferred to Tallaght and they had tried to ring me but of course I wasn't at home, as I was at work. I caught up with him as he was being helped into the ambulance and he whispered to me 'Mammy, sign me out and I'll go back to my apartment.' I said 'I can't do that love, it wouldn't be right for you.' My heart was breaking as they drove him away. He was my son and I felt I had let him down, but what could I do? I drove up to Dublin to my mother in floods of tears.

"However, as far as David was concerned the transfer to Tallaght was the best thing that happened to him. Hospital just isn't an option for him but in Tallaght he met Dr. Finian Kelly and through him the team in the Clondalkin Centre and they've never let go of him since.

"He attended the day hospital and they stabilised him on medication and did home visits and he was able to go back to work and he was great for three or four months.

"Then in December he began to complain that the medication was making him drowsy and he needed a clear head for work and for a holiday he was planning in the United States. He went off on holidays and must have given up the medication. When he came back he told us someone had mugged him and thrown him up against a tree. We never knew if it really happened or not. He also said he'd had a few drinks and he never drank, so you wouldn't know what happened out there.

"I rang them in Clondalkin and between us we persuaded to go back to the Day Hospital a couple of months ago. They kept on trying to engage with him but he wouldn't keep appointments. I was trying to act as a liaison but then he turned against me and said I was in league with the staff against him. Then he had a call from work and he was told that he would have to have treatment, so now he is going to the Day Hospital every day.

"We are all so lucky to have found the Clinic. The people here are absolutely marvellous. This illness is completely foreign to the son I knew. It is a horrible selfish illness, it takes over a person's mind and they move away completely from reality. I am learning more about mental illness every day and that is very important for us all. I can go to the support group and ask any questions I want there or here in the clinic.

"Margeret (Downey) and Finian (Kelly) and Ken (Nunn) are wonderful. When David became ill, it was like he became my little boy again and I thought that maybe to mother him was the way to go. My maternal instincts kicked in but it didn't work and I am in limbo now. I have to back off and hand him over to the professionals. It's hard because I'm not a part-time mother who goes off duty when times get bad.

"David has hidden his illness so long. He became a master at it until his physical body couldn't take it any longer and he had to give way to the overwhelming tiredness It is hard because he is such a good boy, somebody who never hurt anybody in his life. He just doesn't deserve this.

"I know he is in marvellous hands in the Clinic. I see them as a family with Finian as the father, Margaret as the mother and the rest of the team the children. Mary who retired in September was also so good to him. I was worried about him one Sunday recently and Finian came in to help. It is amazing that we have access to the doctors and nurses at any time because when things go wrong it is often at night or at weekends when you'd expect them to be off duty, but they are always there for us.

"David needs a lot of help. I am still very worried about him but I know we all have the best care and support we can have here."

19

The Clondalkin Mental Health Service Team in 2010

The Clondalkin Mental Health Service (CMHS) team is dedicated to providing the highest quality community-based psychiatric service for adults with severe and enduring mental illness, giving a choice of care programmes, with an emphasis on providing support and education for patients and their families/carers. The team also acts as a resource for primary care and other agencies, providing consultation, guidance and advice.

The Clondalkin Mental Health Service team provides a service to a catchment area of over 60,000 people, covering the whole of the Clondalkin area and also parts of south county Dublin, including Saggart, Brittas and Newcastle. The current team makeup is illustrated in the table on the following page.

The team works as a team. No individual team member works in isolation, no patient therapy is individual to one member of the team. All treatment is shared and supported, and devised to bring maximal benefit to the recovery of our service users. The continued development of the therapeutic relationship between the community team and our

CMHS Staffing in 2010

1 Consultant Psychiatrist	
Day Hospital	1 CNM2
	1 staff nurse
Home Care Team	1 CNM2
	0.5 CNM1
	1 Clinical Nurse Specialist
	4 Staff Nurses
Day Centre	1 CNM2
	1 staff nurse
3 CMHNs (2 of whom job-share)	
1 Occupational Therapist	
1 Social Worker	
1 Psychologist	
2 Administrative staff	
0.5 Household staff	
Dietician: one session fortnightly	
Students from all disciplines	
1 Senior Registrar	
1 Psychiatry Registrars	
1 GP trainee Registrar	

patients will continue sometimes over a period of several years in those with more severe or complicated illness.

In keeping with its ethos of being integral to the community it serves, since 1992 the Clondalkin Mental Health Service has operated from the heart of Clondalkin village, from premises at Unit 1A Village Centre, Orchard Road. The Day Hospital, the Home Care Team and the Community Mental Health Nurses operate from these premises, known as the Clondalkin Mental Health Centre (CMHC).

The Mental Health Centre is also where new referrals are assessed at the Thursday morning New Patient Clinic. Because of limitations in the size of the Orchard Road premises, we run our return outpatient clinics in the Rowagh Health Centre in north Clondalkin on Wednesday mornings.

Although we have access to inpatient beds in the Adelaide and Meath Hospital in Tallaght, the Clondalkin team is dedicated to treatment of patients in the community, in their own homes and their own environment, and hospitalisation is used only if absolutely necessary. Thus the inpatient service is reserved for the seriously mentally ill who because of severity of acute illness, or danger to self or others, cannot be managed in the community.

The great majority of patients who are acutely ill will not require hospitalisation. When a patient is admitted to hospital, therapeutic emphasis is on early continuation of care in the community. Therefore duration of inpatient treatment tends to be short. Inpatients often attend the Day Hospital from the ward, transitioning quickly into the community and often to shared care with the Home Care Team and the Community Mental Health Nurses.

The Day Hospital provides intensive treatment of acutely ill patients, equivalent to that available in a hospital in-patient setting. Whilst the Day Hospital is primarily for treatment of patients with acute psychiatric disorders, it is also used for assessment of new patients or patients with unclear presentations, allowing longitudinal assessments, which allow clarification of presentation, symptomatology and diagnosis.

Up to eight patients attend the Day Hospital at any one time, but flexible working practices, based on clinical needs, allow more patients to attend occasionally. Patients are reviewed daily by the Day Hospital nurses and a doctor. Individual treatment plans are drawn up following multidisciplinary assessment. Psychoeducation is always a key component of these treatment plans. There are group activities but individual therapy is also provided. Medication is usually supervised during the period of Day hospital attendance. The management and progress of the Day Hospital patients is reviewed and discussed by the whole team at the twice-weekly multi-disciplinary team meetings.

Duration of treatment in the Day Hospital tends to be brief, with pre-admission treatment and discharge planning essential to ensure that this resource is used in an optimally effective manner. The average duration of attendance at the Day hospital is two weeks.

The team currently has three Community Mental Health Nurses (CMHNs), two of whom job share. The CMHNs have an average case load of 30 patients at any one time. They monitor the patients with severe enduring illness who have gained symptom stability, alert for any signs of relapse or recurrence of illness.

The CMHNs are expert in developing positive relationships and providing supportive care for patients and families. They become the friends and confidants of the patients and their carers/families, so that they feel enabled to report issues that may signify possible relapse of symptoms. The CMHNs also closely monitor the patients who are on long-acting depot medication, and patients on medication that requires regular investigations, such as lithium or valproate.

The CMHNs are the main source of liaison with community hostels, training centres and other agencies such as housing associations.

The CMHNs have an important crisis intervention role, frequently being the team member who does the initial assessment of a crisis situation in the community. The CMHN then liaises with the team medical staff, the Day Hospital or Home Care as appropriate to organise appropriate treatment. When the patient stabilises the CMHN is there to ensure long term follow up

The Home Care Team delivers a seven-day weekly quality home based treatment package to patients who are acutely unwell with mental health problems. Often the home-care treatment will prevent the need for hospitalisation of severely ill patients. When patients are admitted for inpatient care, the duration of admission can be shortened because the home-care team will continue acute treatment in the patient's own home. Thus, home-care is frequently an alternative to hospitalisation for patients with acute psychiatric presentations.

There are 6.5 nurses in the home-care team (1 CNM2, 0.5 CNM1, 1 Clinical Nurse Specialist, 4 Staff Nurses), with an ADON managing all of the nursing functions in the community team (across Home-care, Day Hospital, Day Centre and the CMHNs).

Each Home Care Team member has an average case load of 10-12 patients, of which 2-3 are acute, the remainder continuing care. The Home Care Team maintains regular contact (daily or twice daily) with the acutely unwell patients in order to monitor their clinical condition and to provide effective treatment and rehabilitation.

When a patient is on Acute Home Care, there will be home visits once or twice daily (and even three times daily if necessary), as dictated by need. Duration of visits varies, depending on the patient's individual needs

In Home Care, treatment emphasis is on symptom management, medication concordance / adherence, psychoeducation and relapse prevention.

As symptoms dissipate and improvement occurs, frequency and duration of visits decrease. The patient is encouraged to take responsibility for his/her own care by attending at the Mental Health Centre for reviews, and by taking responsibility for self medication. After the

*Members of Team 2010 — **Back Row:** Olivia Conden, Fiona Ruane, Paul McShane, Louise Brennan, Gay Lavery, Patricia Freeman, Finian Kelly, Grace Huages, Kathleen O'Sullivan, Vincent Monaghan.*
***Front Row:** Michelle O'Donoghue, Louise Deans, Deirdre Jackson, Margaret Downey, Vincent Nwankwo, Grace McNamee*

acute treatment phase, the patient transfers to home-care continuing care, or to CMHN / outpatient care.

Home Care Continuing care patients tend to be younger patients, often with first presentation of psychiatric illness. They include those patients with severe and enduring mental illness who lack social support, and those with poor adherence to treatment who are likely to serially relapse unless long term intervention is planned. Continuing Care is also provide for a smaller group of patients with significant personality disorders who encounter continuing difficulty in managing and coping with everyday life

The role of the Home Care Nurse is to provide a human link between patient and mental health service; to establish the therapeutic relationship; to assess and care plan to meet the needs of the patient and carers/family; and to provide support and education for the patient and the family/carers.

After the acute treatment phase the patient moves to the Continuing Care phase of Home Care, during which the home-care nurse helps him/her and the family/carers to coordinate use of resources from the mental health service and community-based resources, with the primary aim of preventing relapse of symptoms through this ongoing engagement with the mental health service.

The Day Hospital and the Home Care team do not function as stand-alone treatment modalities. There are constant interactions with the other components of the community treatment team. Often there is shared care between the Day hospital and the Home Care team or the CMHNs. The expertise and particular skills of the social worker, occupational therapist and the psychologist on the community team are fully utilised for patients in treatment in the Day Hospital and on Home Care, their involvement being ensured by the constant feed of communication and information through daily informal staff encounters and the more formal MDT meetings.

There are no paper referrals within the community team, all referrals being done at the twice-weekly multidisciplinary team meetings. This ensures that lines of communication are open and that there is clarity of purpose. It also prevents build up of waiting lists – these do not exist in the Clondalkin team – if a patient needs a particular aspect of treatment in which we have the expertise, he/she gets it.

In parallel to all the acute, sub-acute and continuing treatment modalities carried out by the Clondalkin community team, the team undertakes to rehabilitate the patient to full social functioning and recovery. Thus, interventions at a particular stage of treatment are tailored to the specific patient needs, aimed at developing strengths.

In all of the treatment provided by the Clondalkin team, there is a dynamic rehabilitative process aimed at prevention of long term disability, maintaining social supports and promoting engagement in meaningful occupation.

The day hospital and homecare teams, and the CMHNs, work hand-in–hand with the other disciplines in the team (OT, social worker, psychologist) to carry out needs assessments and to devise consequent appropriate treatment strategies, be they social or vocational, tailored to the individual patient needs and with the aim of achieving as full a recovery as is feasible.

An integral part of this process is appropriate engagement of community resources.

All of these activities are underpinned by a philosophy in the team that patient empowerment and patient advocacy are essential to the patient gaining life autonomy.

The Day Centre provides ongoing support and monitoring for patients with severe and enduring mental illness, who do not require acute care, but who have greater needs than can be provided by the

Anne Flynn (†2010) and Mary McGlynn

outpatient and CMHN follow up. It is located in St Bridget's Road, close to the centre of Clondalkin village. The Day Centre is staffed by one CNM2 and one staff nurse.

The Day Centre provides a safe nurturing environment for the attendees aiming to promote and maintain stable mental health. It helps to reduce the need for hospital admission in a particularly vulnerable group of patients, thus avoiding dependency and institutionalisation. It also provides support to families and carers.

The Day Centre is an activity-based centre with individual and group programmes. Social contact and integration is encouraged in a non-threatening environment. Activities are structured with an achievable end product, and will change depending on the needs of the group. There is a balance between work, leisure, social and self-care activities. Personal care, personal development and home management are all included in group and individual programmes.

Activities may help those who require it to achieve a level of competency in activities of daily living. Liaison with community groups allows patients to access appropriate activities outside of the mental health service.

If necessary, there is supervision of medication in the Day Centre but the ultimate aim, through continuing education regarding illness and medication, is to achieve self-mediation.

Many of the patients attending the Day Centre would become acutely unwell if this facility was not available to support them. Equally, many of them would not be able to live independent lives in the community without the daily support and ongoing therapy provided by the Day Centre.

The CMHS team has additional support from the bank of retired nurses who cover leave and other absences. These experienced nursed are an invaluable addition to our team and their wealth of experience is often called on in managing difficult illnesses and situations.

The CMHS clinical team is lead by a consultant psychiatrist, a specialist in General Adult Psychiatry. There are four other medically qualified members of the team. One Senior Registrar is posted to the team each year; this is a doctor who is in the final stages of higher specialist training before being eligible to become a consultant.

There are two Registrars, doctors specialising in psychiatry following their general medical training, who rotate into different posts every six months. The other medical person is a doctor specialising in General Practice who spends six months with us. This is a vitally important part of the training for a General Practitioner, since the majority of mental health issues present to and are treated by GPs. GPs whose training expose them to the community-based treatment approach of the CMHS are equipped to deal with the reality of managing severe mental illness in the patients own home environment.

There are future plans to develop a new Mental Health Centre in premises that will also be home to several primary care disciplines/functions. This new premises will bring together the disparate parts of the CMHS, such that the Day Centre and the outpatient clinics will be within the same premises as the other components of the service.

Wherever it operates from into the future, the Clondalkin Mental Health Service team will continue to offer the highest quality community-based psychiatric service for adults with severe and enduring mental illness, always aiming at achieving full recovery.

Dr. Finian Kelly[7]

---

7   I would like to acknowledge and thank team members Margaret Downey, Vincent Monaghan, Kathleen O'Sullivan, Gay Lavery, Bernie Williams, Jayne Campbell, James Quah, Maylis Muldoon and Kelly Holmes for their contributions to this chapter.

20

A high flyer

Jessica (not her real name) was, and is, a high flyer. She was a gifted scientist with a brilliant academic career when she suddenly found herself in the middle of a nightmare.

"I was suddenly plunged into this terrifying conspiracy which I couldn't solve and which endangered the people I loved most in the world. When I found out that Russian assassins were hiding in my sister's attic, I rushed 'round there to save her.

"Then there were gangs threatening my parents and blackmailing my friends. They were also trying to put poison in medication at home. There was nobody I could trust and nobody was safe from 'the organisation' which was masterminding this terrible conspiracy. It was all up to me. I was on my own and I was failing to protect and save my family. I thought if I could escape I might be able to do something, so I packed my bags and left home."

A few months earlier, Jessica, who at the time was in her late 20s, had suffered what she and her family thought was a nervous breakdown. They thought she was suffering from a mixture of work related and post traumatic stress factors.

However, a year later the nightmare which she now recognises as a psychotic episode occurred. As a young professional she had been living in town but returned home to live with her parents. Things improved for a while and then the symptoms returned.

"It culminated one day when I actually hit my sister. I thought she was part of the conspiracy and by hitting her I would solve the whole thing. It was all so frightening for her, for the rest of my family and of course for myself. I was holding my niece at the same time which made it all the more terrible.

"Luckily my parents were very sensible. They suggested I go to Tallaght Hospital and I went voluntarily. But again in the hospital it was the same thing. I had to fix things, I thought they would interview me and all the other people and help me to solve the mystery. It was very scary like living in a nightmare when you couldn't save people from danger or control what was happening.

"At this stage I was hallucinating. I thought a person who had been fine a few minutes earlier was covered in bruises and I thought the gang had got to him and injured him. I found the hospital a very distressing environment"

Jessica was in hospital for about 36 hours and was then discharged to the Clondalkin Mental Health Centre.

"Initially, I was seen by Margaret and she was very nice to me. She was so sympathetic and easy to talk to. I would have been apprehensive about some of the doctors, but this was different. I thought I would be with Margaret all the time but then it was explained to me that Jane would be looking after me.

"I thought something bad had happened because of the change of nurse, but they explained to me that this wasn't so and that Margaret had other duties and responsibilities.

"At the beginning Jane came to my home which was great as I still had reservations about whom I could and could not trust. I still thought the gangs were there but I was happy that my parents would be around. I thought that even if they were pressured by the gangs they would look after my interests and not sell me out.

"I would have been so much more distressed if I had been in hospital or even if I had to go down to the Centre at first. I felt safe at home. I wanted my parents to guide me and it was hugely important and comforting for me to be there with my family. I needed routine and familiarity.

"Also I knew that the gangs hadn't bugged my parents' home but I would have thought the hospital was bugged.

"I really warmed to Jane. After a while I started going to the Centre. At first it was every second day, then every two weeks and now I come once a month.

"I would come and have a chat if I had any psychiatric or depressive symptoms. At one time I was having ideas of killing myself but then I thought that if I died there was no way that I could solve the conspiracy. It was a horrible predicament but I could always see a doctor who would go through the issues with me.

"Every time I saw Jane and chatted to her I began to be less paranoid and less fearful. I saw that there were simple explanations for the coincidences which I had seen as a conspiracy. Jane was very pleased with me and said it was a very important step that I realised the things I had feared were not real."

At one stage Jessica was off her medication for about three weeks and she felt the symptoms returning.

"Again, I started to think that something was going on but I knew it wasn't real. I could see lots of people on 'phones relaying information about the conspiracy but I knew it was really perfectly normal behaviour. I was able to maintain control even thought I was not on the medication. But I was eager to get back on the medication.

"My current medication produces no side effects to me and I am quite happy to stay on it for a year or two, as it should produce a total remission by then.

"I have been and am very comforted that I can come around here rather than having to go to hospital. I can drop in on my way to work

"It's wonderful to have Jane's support. When I told her what happened when I was off the medication she told me it was good that I was able to control the symptoms and that helped me greatly.

"I have Jane's 'phone number and have given it to my Mum and my sister, so if any of us notices that I am getting the symptoms back we can ring her.

"Jane also offered that my parents could come down and chat. I am very happy that I can come and talk to her every week. She identifies positives and comments on how well I am doing.

"Life has improved a lot and I have been getting on very well. I was very concerned that I might not be able to lead a 'normal' life because the two psychotic episodes happened so closely. But now I know I can. Work is going well and I am out socialising. I have much for which I am thankful – my good life, my wonderful family, Jane and the Clondalkin Mental Health Centre."

21

The Neighbours
An interview with Dr. Clare O'Toole

Clondalkin Mental Health Service has an ethos of working with the community and in doing so drawing on the skills and supports of the voluntary agencies in the area. Throughout the years the patients of Clondalkin Mental Health Service have benefited greatly from the availability of and access to local voluntary agencies.

Voluntary activity has always had a prominent role in the delivery of health and social services in Ireland and this is particularly evident in the Clondalkin area. The strength of the community is reflected in the number of voluntary organisations and social enterprises that have emerged over time in response to new needs, demonstrating an effort by the people of Clondalkin to find local solutions to local problems.

Examples of voluntary agencies whose work complements that of Clondalkin Mental Health Service include the Housing Association for Integrated Living (HAIL), Beacon of Light Counselling Service, Pieta House, Bawnogue Women's Development Group and Clondalkin Addiction Support Programme (CASP) to mention just a few.

The important role played by the community and voluntary sector in Ireland has been highlighted in a number of important reports. The Commission on Health Funding in 1989 highlighted the "immensely important" role of voluntary organisations and referred to their community spirit, humanitarianism and closeness to the client group. The Health Strategy 1994 stated that the voluntary sector "plays an integral role in the provision of health and personal social services in Ireland which is perhaps unparalleled in any other country". The 2000 Government White Paper on the relationship between the state and the voluntary sector noted that "an active community and voluntary sector contributes to a democratic, pluralist society, provides opportunities for the development of a decentralised and participative structure and fosters a climate in which the quality of life can be enhanced for all".

Similarly, the 2006 National Economic and Social Council Strategy stressed the need for "healthy community and voluntary organisations" as "an important requirement for overall economic and social development. The national partnership agreement Towards 2016 reflects similar sentiments stating that "the Government recognises that community and voluntary activity forms the very core of a vibrant and inclusive society".

It is the ethos and values of voluntary organisations that distinguish them from state provided organisations; they typically become involved in areas neglected by the state or fulfil gaps in public and social services. They frequently build up expertise in certain areas, developing specialist skills and expertise and in so doing are invaluable resources to their local community. They have a valuable contribution to make in complementing the work done by state provided services.

This mutually beneficial relationship is demonstrated in the way Clondalkin Mental Health Service has engaged with local voluntary agencies. These relationships have developed gradually over time and the benefits of collaborative working impact positively on the quality of care received by the community.

I would like to touch on some of "the neighbours", the voluntary agencies in Clondalkin whose work is of huge benefit to many patients presenting to the Clondalkin Mental Health Service.

The Beacon of Light Counselling Centre was founded by Sr. Patricia Kidd in 1994. It is a community-based project which provides high quality, accessible and affordable professional counselling and workshops.

The service started out from one little room in the back of St. Peter the Apostle Church in the Neilstown area. As the clear need and demand for this valuable service emerged, Sr. Kidd was joined in 1999 by Maureen O'Mahoney, who currently manages the service which has continued to expand and established itself firmly in Clondalkin.

Over the past nine years or so, the Beacon of Light Counselling Centre has become an important part of the community infrastructure in the greater Clondalkin area. It is located in the heart of the community, working from two houses, one in Collinstown Grove and in the past two years from a second house in Balgaddy.

The Beacon of Light receives referrals from many statutory agencies such as Clondalkin Mental Health Service, GP practices and schools and community development groups in Clondalkin. It assists and supports individuals going through difficult life experiences – such as bereavement, anxiety, depression, those dealing with addiction issues, those at risk of suicide or coping with such loss. It offers family and individual counselling as well as educational and personal development work. Its clients range in age from six years to those in their 70s.

The Beacon of Light offers their services at an affordable rate, clients pay according to their means and their capacity to pay. Funding comes from a variety of different sources and at present the Beacon of Light does not have any core ongoing funding. In 2009 its main contributors were Clondalkin Drugs Task Force, Unilever, Dormant Accounts Fund, and the Family Support Agency. Fundraising and client contributions are other sources of funding.

Its staffing consists of 28 volunteer counsellors and seven part-time counsellors. In 2009 it provided 4,490 counselling sessions to 508 clients. The service operates extended opening hours open from 9.00am to 9.00pm Monday through Thursday.

Over the last couple of years Sr. Kidd has noticed an increase in the numbers of people presenting with issues related to suicide and parasuicide.

She also said that the strengthening of a relationship with Clondalkin Mental Health Service, particularly in the last two years, has been helpful especially in managing complex cases. It is a mutually beneficial relationship as many of those presenting to Clondalkin Mental Health Service with psychological issues, life stresses or loneliness, benefit from the counselling and family work offered by the Beacon of Light.

These needs are recognised by Clondalkin Mental Health Service but as the service focus is on dealing with more severe mental illness it is not in a position to provide this much needed service, also. However through appropriate referral and collaborative working between Clondalkin Mental Health Service and the Beacon of Light on certain cases the optimal use of available resources can be achieved.

Pieta House is a service developed for people with self harm or suicidal thoughts or behaviours. It was established in 2006 by Joan Freeman, a psychologist by training, who saw a gap in services. The service is provided free to the client by volunteers, accredited psychotherapists or counsellors.

Pieta House offers a holistic solution involving daily one-to-one counselling for people who have attempted to take their own lives or for people who have engaged in self-harming behaviours. Pieta House provide coping mechanisms for people who are in crisis and aims to move the suicidal person away from ideas of suicide as quickly as possible by helping them identify reasons to live.

Pieta House has dealt with in excess of 3,000 clients since the service began. The service has 32 counsellors at present, but reflecting increasing demand, it is due to expand to 50 counsellors with the opening of centres in Limerick, Tallaght, Finglas and Ballyfermot later this year.

Joan Freeman says they have a great relationship with Dublin West/South West mental health service and the various consultants within it, including Dr Ian Daly, Dr Finian Kelly and Dr Anne O'Grady Walshe.

Pieta House receives a large number of referrals from Tallaght Hospital and the various mental health clinics associated with it in addition to self referrals, referrals from schools, GP practices etc. There are proposals to formalise the relationship with the mental health services further with the "Gatekeeper model" which will involve the introduction of two suicide prevention nurse posts in Tallaght Hospital. Interestingly Joan mentioned that Pieta House receive e-mail enquiries from all over the world reflecting the universal nature of the work being done at this centre. It is clearly an asset for the people of Clondalkin to have access to such a resource.

HAIL – Housing Association for Integrated Living, is a voluntary agency which has approved status from the Department of the Environment, Heritage & Local Government. It was set up as a limited company with charitable status and is another voluntary organisation, the role of which is hugely important to Clondalkin Mental Health Service.

HAIL primarily provides an appropriate and specialised housing service for people with mental health difficulties; it also provides some general needs accommodation for wheelchair users.

It was founded in 1985 by members of the Housing Committee of St Brendan's Mental Health Association. It provides secure permanent housing for families and single people and a visiting support service for people with mental health difficulties. HAIL provides housing in each of the Local Authority areas in the greater Dublin area and has recently expanded to Co. Kildare, in partnership with Respond, a sister Housing Association. HAIL provides a full tenancy agreement to the people they house.

Over the three decades of its existence, HAIL has built up relationships with the various mental health services in the greater Dublin area. HAIL has had a base in Clondalkin for about 11 years now. Sean Megahey, Services Manager, says the relationship with the local mental health team in Clondalkin is hugely important in supporting the work they do. Staff from HAIL and Clondalkin Mental Health Service work together in many ways when dealing with clients around their housing needs.

Community psychiatric nurses have a role in identifying suitable clients for referral when accommodation units are coming on stream. There is a support piece when clients are transitioning to HAIL accommodation both from HAIL support workers and the community psychiatric nurses, while clients adjust to their new environment.

The link between HAIL and the Community Mental Health Team is important where there is concern about possible relapse and this is effectively dealt with through good relationships and open 'phone communication. HAIL and the Community Mental Health Team also work together when a property is vacant, due to hospitalisation and in preparation for discharge.

Referrals to HAIL come from relevant social services in the area such as the mental health services. HAIL also takes referrals from housing associations providing transitional housing or hostel accommodation such as FOCUS Ireland, SIMON etc.

Funding comes from capital funding from Department of Environment, Heritage & Local Government under the schemes available to the voluntary and co-operative housing sector. It also receives funding from the Homeless Agency and the HSE towards the provision of its Settlement/Support service to assist tenants integrate into their local communities, maintain links with mainstream physical and mental health services, maximise social, educational and employment opportunities thereby sustaining their tenancies.

The developments are not fully funded so this is supplemented by fundraising events such as flag days, coffee mornings, and mini marathons. HAIL also receives donations from various charitable trusts e.g. People in Need Trust and Katherine Howard Foundation.

HAIL has properties around Dublin from Tallaght to Clondalkin, Ballymun and Raheny and has recently acquired apartments in Celbridge in partnership with Respond. HAIL is a hugely valuable organisation for the people of Clondalkin who have mental health needs and who require support around independent living. There is no doubt that many of those individuals housed by HAIL would spend more time in hospital or other mental health facilities or in homeless accommodation were it not for the valuable work being done by HAIL.

There are many other agencies in the Clondalkin area which facilitate Clondalkin Mental Health Service focus on the severe mental illness by providing supports to those with related difficulties.

These include Clondalkin Addiction Support Programme (CASP) which was established in 1995 in response to increasing numbers of young heroin users in Clondalkin, It is a community service for drug users and their families in the North Clondalkin area and has proved a useful resource where drug addiction issues appear to be the primary problem for those referred to Clondalkin Mental Health Service.

Bawnogue Women's Development Group is another useful organisation that provides support for many of the young women with social isolation, parenting and other social issues.

While not actually a voluntary agency, a very important neighbour in the day to day activity of the Clondalkin Mental Health team is the Clubhouse. The Clubhouse operated under the auspices of EVE Holdings and was a copy of the Clubhouse movement first started in New York. The organising principle was that people who had mental health difficulties would run their own job finding and job preparation service and also receive social opportunities and offer mutual support.

"The neighbours" have an invaluable role to play in facilitating Clondalkin Mental Health Service to provide comprehensive community-based mental health care. The diversity of voluntary services catering for a variety of life difficulties ensures that a whole person approach can be taken when identifying the most suitable options and services to meet an individual's needs. As services mature, relationships are strengthening and formalising – meaning a simple phone call is all it takes to connect – and so work in partnership with the voluntary agencies in the area. There is no doubt that as new problems emerge the men and women of Clondalkin will continue to take ownership of the challenges they face and respond by developing new voluntary services to meet the needs of their community.

Dr. Clare O'Toole, Locum Consultant Psychiatrist, Dublin West / South West Mental Health services

22

A year in the life

In 2009 the Clondalkin Mental Health Service provided adult psychiatric care to a sector with a population of 65,000 persons, covering a wide geographical area around Clondalkin including Rathcoole, Brittas, Saggart and Balgaddy. This encompassed areas of social deprivation and high unemployment, often untouched by the Celtic tiger. There are very high rates of drug and alcohol abuse and in 2009 the problem of "Head Shop" psychoactive substances added to the work of the Clondalkin Mental Health team.

During the calendar year 2009 more than 850 patients were assessed and treated by the Clondalkin Mental Health Service. During the year, there were 495 referrals to the service, 18% of these from emergency departments of the local hospitals (mainly AMNCH, also St James's and Connolly hospitals). Over 80% of referrals to the service were from general practitioners.

Of the 495 referrals, 349 attended for assessment; thus 29% of referred individuals failed to attend. Of the 349 referrals seen, 104 (30%) were discharged back to their GP after assessment, with advice for future management. The remaining 245 patients were taken on for treatment by the CMHS team, usually for specific defined treatment over a limited period of care.

The most frequent diagnosis amongst the new referrals was depression or anxiety (43%), with significant numbers presenting with substance abuse and adjustment disorders (see Table 1).

Table 1: Diagnoses in 349 attendees

Depression/anxiety	43%
Alcohol/substance	17%
Adjustment disorder	16%
Psychosis	9%
Personality disorder	5%
PTSD	3%
Eating disorder	1%
No psychiatric illness	5%
Drugs/alcohol a factor	in 58% of referrals

Of note is that alcohol or substance abuse was a known factor in the presentation of 58% of the referrals – thus it is likely that the true frequency of these problems is higher in reality, since not all alcohol and substance abuse is revealed, likely to be implicated in 70% of referrals.

At any one time in 2009, there were over 500 patients attending the Clondalkin Mental Health Service and at the end of 2009 there were 520 patients in active treatment. The diagnostic categories of these patients are shown in Table 2

Table 2: Principle Diagnosis in 520 patients

Schizophrenia	114
BPAD	88
Schizoaffective	19
Other psychoses	34
EUPD	24

Inpatient admission

There were 84 admissions from the Clondalkin sector to the acute inpatient unit in AMNCH in 2009, 40 females and 44 males. The average duration of inpatient admission was 7.1 nights (range 1-112), down from an average of 11.8 nights in 2008. This duration of stay was substantially shorter, by a factor of more than 50%, than each of the adjoining sectors in the Dublin West/Southwest Psychiatric Service, with 19 admissions of just one night and 51% of the admissions being of less than 5 days duration.

Most of the hospital admissions (71%) were via the Emergency Department. Thus less than 30% of admissions were arranged by the community team. Those admissions which were via the Emergency Department were shorter in length of stay and had diagnoses in the less serious categories of psychiatric illness. In most cases, for the admissions that were not organised by the Clondalkin Team it was clear that inpatient treatment was not necessary and was not the optimum modality of treatment.

Involuntary admissions were almost all organised by the Clondalkin Team and reflect the most severely ill patients in the service, with diagnoses mainly of acute psychotic episodes (often schizophreniform in nature) and mania.

Day hospital

During 2009 there was an increase in patients attending the day hospital for acute treatment of psychiatric illness. There were 111 admissions with a mean duration of treatment of two weeks and a total of 1,807 daily attendances. The average duration of attendance at the day hospital has increased in 2009, with 32% of patients attending for more than three weeks, reflecting the more serious cases of depression and acute psychotic episodes.

Diagnoses were as follows:

Schizophrenia	24
Depression	24
Bipolar disorder	20
Adjustment disorder	11
Schizoaffective:	6
Other psychoses	7
Substance or alcohol abuse/dependence	37

Home care

During 2009 there were 147 patients on acute homecare treatment, 87 of whom had had previous periods of homecare, and 60 new patients. The period of acute treatment was generally 20-30 days, with 32% of acute cases continuing to longer-term continuing care with the home-care team. Thirty percent of acute homecare patients were discharged from the service after the period of acute homecare treatment, an indicator of the effectiveness of this kind of treatment

The diagnoses in the 147 patients who were on acute homecare in 2009 were as follows:

BPAD	41
Schizophrenia	32
Other psychoses	19
Depression	26
Postnatal depression	8
Personality disorders	7
Schizoaffective disorder	6
Psychotic depression	4
Drug-induced psychosis	3

Out-patient clinic

The outpatient clinic is held once weekly in Rowlagh health centre in North Clondalkin. The clinic is run by the community mental health nurses, with assessments being done by the medical team. The clinic functions as an opportunity to screen patients with serious mental illness for stability, and to afford continuing support and therapy to those patients.

The average attendance at the weekly out-patient clinic in 2009 was 56 patients. Seventy-one patients were receiving depot antipsychotic medication at the outpatient clinic, at 2-4 weekly intervals. Patients on lithium (n=52) and valproate (n=52) are monitored at the outpatient clinic and appropriate investigations are done according to standard protocols.

Day centre

The day centre caters for patients with serious illness who need psychosocial stimulation, and assistance with symptom management and medication. In 2009 11-14 patients attended the day centre daily. There were 1,865 total daily attendances. There were 12 new referrals during the year with 7 discharges. There are now 20 patients attending, mainly with a diagnosis of schizophrenia.

Allied disciplines

As in all functioning psychiatric multidisciplinary teams, the occupational therapist, social worker and clinical psychologist work seamlessly with all the acute and continuing care components of the treatment team.

The average caseload of the occupational therapist in 2009 was 20 patients per month. Several of these patients were taken on for individual work and others were treated in groups. Referrals came from homecare, day hospital, OPD and CMHNs. Most of the patients had a diagnosis of schizophrenia or psychosis. The typical duration of attendance was from 12-16 weeks.

Most of the referrals to the team social worker came from the home care team and the day hospital. Referrals tend to be young single males and females. A large range of issues are dealt with by the social worker, including child protection issues, child care and parenting problems, housing/accommodation problems and, increasingly, financial and social benefits issues. There was a notable increase in the number of patients referred who were from the new Irish community.

There were almost 80 referrals to the team's clinical psychologist in 2009. Three-quarters of these patients were seen for assessment or therapy and the remainder on a consultation basis. Over half of the patients were taken on for therapy and almost 100% attendance was achieved, indicating the appropriateness of referrals and effectiveness of the initial assessment process. The most frequent diagnosis was depression or anxiety, but there were also a number of patients with personality disorders, OCD, traumas and psychosis/schizophrenia taken on. The age range was from 17 – 84 years. Fifty-six per cent of patients were referred from out-patients, 23% from homecare, 16% from the day hospital and 5% from the in-patient unit. During the year there appeared to be an increase in younger patients with personality disorders, eating disorders or self harm.

Group activities

There are several groups being run on an ongoing basis by the Clondalkin Team. The Stay-Well Group is an early rehabilitation intervention aimed at young, newly diagnosed patients with severe and enduring mental illness, aiming to enhance their present quality of living and ultimately lead a more fulfilled life. The Stay-Well objectives are achieved by providing a streamlined programme based on the principles of wellness and recovery

The Carers' Group has been running since the start of the Clondalkin Project. This is an educational and support group for the carers and families of service users. It is run in the evening and is a source of great support for the participants.

The Walking Group meets twice weekly in a local park, and occasionally further afield. It is aimed at those service users who identified exercise and social interaction as goals but were unable to participate because of other difficulties such as demotivation, anxiety, social isolation, poor self efficacy or limited opportunities

No patients are excluded and it has proved a particular success with persons with personality disorders.

The A1 Group was set up to encourage younger patients to interact socially. It aims to normalise their illness experiences. It uses local resources and aims at community integration. Types of activity include walking, day trips, cinema and snooker. It has evolved to include those with varying levels of distress.

Other groups include the children of service users group and the anxiety management group.

Dr. Finian Kelly[8]

8   I would like to acknowledge and thank team members Margaret Downey, Vincent Monaghan, Kathleen O'Sullivan, Bernie Williams, John Brennan, Jayne Campbell, James Quah, Joan Walker, Aisling Walshe, Maylis Muldoon and Kelly Holmes for their contributions to this chapter.